THE OFFICIAL
MANCHESTER UNITED®
Spelling
Book

LOUIS FIDGE

KICK-OFF

The Manchester United books are a fun way to learn and practise your English skills. Each book contains: 11 Big Matches, a flick-a-book player, find the cup, a poster and a board game!

The Big Matches

Learn a new skill

Practise the skill

Flick the pages and make the player move

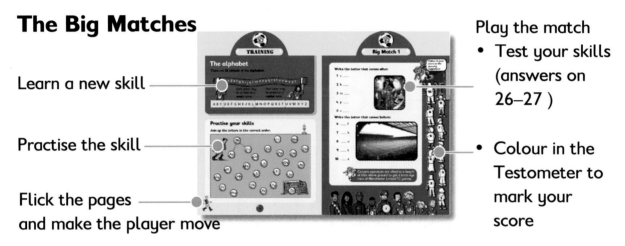

Play the match
- Test your skills (answers on 26–27)

- Colour in the Testometer to mark your score

See if you can find the cup hidden somewhere in each unit

Enjoy the pull-out game and poster in the middle of the book!

The Game

What you need and how to play

The Poster

Collect all the books in the series and the six individual posters make one big poster!

Contents

TRAINING

The alphabet

There are **26 letters** of the **alphabet**.

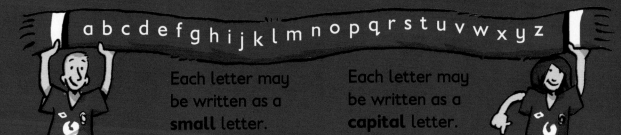

a b c d e f g h i j k l m n o p q r s t u v w x y z

Each letter may be written as a **small** letter.

Each letter may be written as a **capital** letter.

A B C D E F G H I J K L M N O P Q R S T U V W X Y Z

Practise your skills

Join up the letters in the correct order.

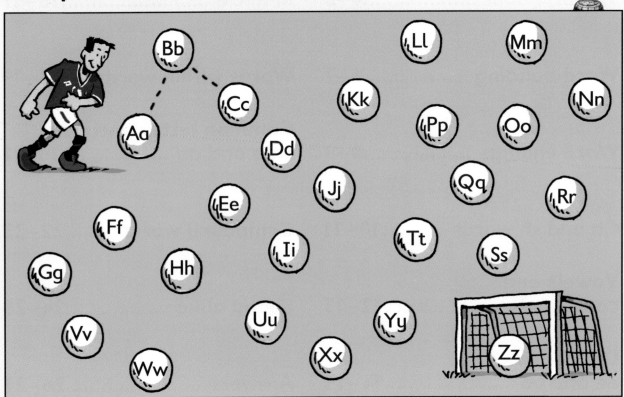

Big Match 1

Colour in your score on the queuing supporters!

Write the letter that comes after:

1 c ____

2 h ____

3 m ____

4 p ____

5 v ____

Write the letter that comes before:

6 ____ f

7 ____ k

8 ____ o

9 ____ t

10 ____ x

 Camera operators are lifted to a height of 65m above ground to get a birds-eye view of Manchester United FC games.

TRAINING

Word–building

We put **letters together** to make **words**.

r + e + d = red

s + i + x = six

r + u + n = run

Practise your skills

A Make the words.

1 b + a + g = _bag_   2 f + a + n = _____   3 w + e + t = _____

4 s + i + t = _____   5 c + u + p = _____   6 n + e + t = _____

B Use the words you have made above. Write each word under the correct picture.

1    2    3

_____   _____   _____

4   5    6

_____   _____   _____

Big Match 2

Write the words you make.

1 c + a + p = _____

2 l + e + g = _____

3 w + i + n = _____

4 h + i + t = _____

5 l + o + b = _____

6 n + o + d = _____

7 b + o + x = _____

8 s + u + b = _____

9 m + u + d = _____

10 h + a + t = _____

Sometimes the grass at Old Trafford is cut three times a week.

10

9

8

7

6

5

4

3

1

2

7

TRAINING

Word endings

Some **short** words **end** with **double letters**.

pass the ball

Practise your skills

A Make these words.

1 b → a → ll _ball_   2 w → a → ll _____   3 f → a → ll _____

4 o → ff _____   5 m → i → ss _____   6 t → o → ss _____

B Use the words you have made above to write the best word to fill each gap.

1 make a _____   2 take a _____   3 kick a _____

4 _____ a coin   5 _____ a penalty   6 send _____

Big Match 3

Colour in your score on the exercising players!

Write the word that rhymes.

will   pull   call   loll   yell

1 ball _____

2 fill _____

3 sell _____

4 doll _____

5 bull _____

less   moss   puff   kiss   cliff

6 huff _____

7 sniff _____

8 mess _____

9 hiss _____

10 boss _____

Manchester United sells 34,750 season tickets a year.

9

Ch and sh words

Whenever the letters **ch** or **sh** **come together** they make **one** sound.
Many words contain **ch** or **sh**.

Man**ch**ester United won the **ch**ampion**sh**ip.

Practise your skills

Make some ch and sh words.

1

ch

_____ ch ip   _____in   _____est   cat_____   pit_____

chip   _____   _____   _____   _____

2

sh

_____ot   _____ip   _____ock   ru_____   wi_____

_____   _____   _____   _____   _____

Big Match 4

Colour in your score on the coaches!

Choose the word from the scarf that means:

chat   child   chest   match   bench

1 part of the body _____

2 something you sit on _____

3 a boy or a girl _____

4 to talk _____

5 a game of football _____

shut   shop   shin   rush   cash

6 to hurry _____

7 where you can buy things _____

8 part of the leg _____

9 a word for money _____

10 not open _____

TRAINING

Vowels and consonants

There are 5 **vowels**: **a**, **e**, **i**, **o** and **u**.
All the other letters are called **consonants**.

Manchester United

vowels

Practise your skills

Choose the missing vowel to complete each word.

1

Fr_e_d

Fred

2
k___ck

_____

3
cl___p

_____

4

h___g

_____

5
sp___t

_____

6

s___ng

_____

Big Match 5

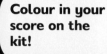

Colour in your score on the kit!

Fill in the missing vowels to spell the names of these Manchester United players.

1 W___s Br___wn

2 N___cky B___tt

3 D___v___d B___ckh___m

4 ___ndy C___l___

5 Ry___n G___ggs

6 R___y K___ ___n___

7 G___ry N___v___ll___

8 P___ ___l Sch___l___s

9 Dw___ght Y___rk___

10 L___k___ Ch___dw___ck

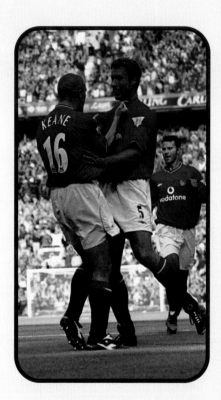

After a match up to six players at a time can relax in a giant bath with bubbling water.

Double vowels ee and oo

Many words contain the double vowels **ee** and **oo**.

Players wear b**oo**ts on their f**ee**t.

Practise your skills

Find and write the ee and oo words.

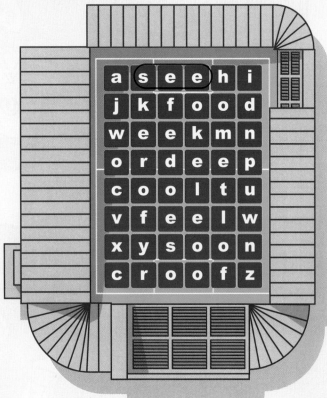

1	see
2	
3	
4	
5	
6	
7	
8	

Good Luck!

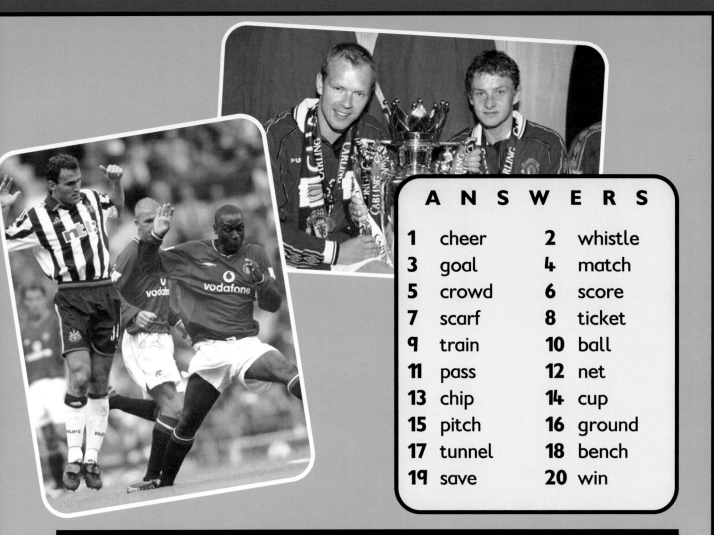

A N S W E R S

1	cheer	2	whistle
3	goal	4	match
5	crowd	6	score
7	scarf	8	ticket
9	train	10	ball
11	pass	12	net
13	chip	14	cup
15	pitch	16	ground
17	tunnel	18	bench
19	save	20	win

How to play

- The aim of the game is to spell the words correctly and win the Championship!
- You need a coin and two counters.
- Take it in turns to throw the coin.
- Start at the bottom of the league table.
  Heads = move up one space.
  Tails = move up two spaces.
- When you land on a word, choose the correct letters to complete it. (Your opponent should check the answers.)
- If you get it wrong – miss a turn.
- The first person to reach the top wins the Championship!

Game

league position	choose the letters	spell the word
1	ee or oo	ch___r
2	ch or wh	___istle
3	oa or ea	g___l
4	i or a	m__tch
5	o or a	cr___wd
6	or or ir	sc___e
7	er or ar	sc___f
8	i or u	t__cket
9	ay or ai	tr___n
10	a or o	b__ll
11	s or ss	pa__
12	f or n	__et
13	p or b	chi__
14	e or u	c__p
15	i or o	p__tch
16	ou or ow	gr___nd
17	n or nn	tu__el
18	ch or sh	ben___
19	a or o	s__ve
20	m or n	wi__

Big Match 6

Colour in your score on the scarf!

Choose **ee** or **oo** to complete each word.
Write each word you make in full.

1 thr _____ _____

2 m _____ n _____

3 k _____ p _____

4 m _____ d _____

5 r _____ t _____

6 gr _____ n _____

7 br _____ m _____

8 sw _____ t _____

9 ch _____ k _____

10 pr _____ f _____

1,316 white seats and 479 black seats are used to spell out Manchester United in the North Stand.

10
9
8
7
6
5
4
3
2
1

15

Magic e

When we add **e** to the **end** of many **short** words,
it makes the **vowel in the middle say its own name**.

kit

kite

kit + e = kite

Practise your skills

Make the words.

1

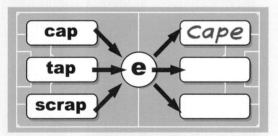

2

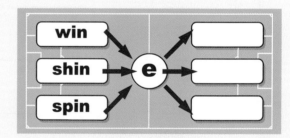

3

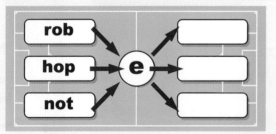

4

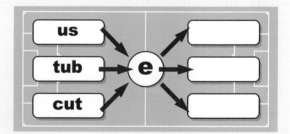

The roof of the North Stand is
so big that the Old Trafford
pitch could fit on top of it.

Big Match 7

Colour in your score on the cones and striker!

Match up the magic e words that rhyme.

1	game			joke
2	line			cube
3	stroke			same
4	tube			make
5	take			fine
6	side			stone
7	time			duke
8	dive			crime
9	bone			wide
10	fluke			five

Words within words

Sometimes you can find **smaller words** **'hiding'** inside longer words.

<u>Man</u><u>chest</u>er

man   chest

Practise your skills

Underline any small words you can find in the players' names.

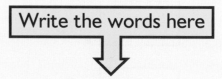
Write the words here

1	Nev<u>ill</u>e	ill
2	Beckham	
3	Irwin	
4	Scholes	
5	Barthez	
6	Fortune	
7	Silvestre	
8	Chadwick	

Big Match 8

Write the words you are left with.

1 Take away 'sel' from 'selfish' _____

2 Take away 'ch' from catch _____

3 Take away 'ard' from 'coward' _____

4 Take away 's' from 'share' _____

5 Take away 'gi' from 'giant' _____

6 Take away 'sc' from 'scowl' _____

7 Take away 'gr' from 'grape' _____

8 Take away 'stif' from 'stiffly' _____

9 Take away 'tle' from 'battle' _____

10 Take away 'dande' from 'dandelion' _____

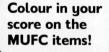

Colour in your score on the MUFC items!

Common letter patterns – ea and oa

You can find the **ea** and **oa** letter patterns in lots of words.

The Manchester United t**ea**m score lots of g**oa**ls.

Practise your skills

Use these words in the crossword puzzle.

seat   beat   cheat   team   coat   goal   boast   coach

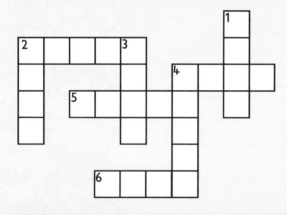

Across	Down
2 To brag	**1** You score this
4 You wear this	**2** To win
5 He teaches footballers	**3** There are 11 football players in this _____
6 You sit on this	**4** It's not fair to do this

Big Match 9

Colour in your score on the film of the match!

Choose **ea** or **oa** to complete each word.
Write each word you make.

1 g____l   _____

2 h____t   _____

3 c____st   _____

4 l____p   _____

5 sp____k   _____

6 cl____k   _____

7 gr____n   _____

8 st____m   _____

9 d____l   _____

10 s____p   _____

The builders used 4,000 tonnes of steel and 4,500 tonnes of concrete to build the North Stand.

21

TRAINING

Compound words

A **compound word** is made up of **two smaller words** joined together.

foot + ball = football

Practise your skills

Write each compound word you make under the correct picture.

goal + keeper   turn + stile   grounds + man

photo + graph   flood + lights   bath + tub

1

2

3

_____photograph_____   _____   _____

4

5

6

_____   _____   _____

Big Match 10

Join up the words. Write the compound words you make.

champion	yard	1 _____
farm	way	2 _____
car	ship	3 <u>championship</u>
motor	port	4 _____
air	pet	5 _____
over	noon	6 _____
under	head	7 _____
after	fly	8 _____
run	ground	9 _____
butter	way	10 _____

TRAINING

Sound alike

Some letter patterns **sound alike** but are spelt **differently**!

Each shirt has a different number.

Practise your skills

Make some words. Write each word you make.

1

er

und **er**   ov___   play___   sw___ve   p___fect

___**under**___   _____   _____   _____   _____

2

ir

sh___t   d___ty   b___d   f___st   g___l

_____   _____   _____   _____   _____

24

Big Match 11

Colour in your score on the winning players!

Choose the correct word.

| striker | defender | goalkeeper | manager | referee |

1 He stops goals being scored. _____

2 Andy Cole is one. _____

3 He makes sure the game is played fairly. _____

4 Alex Ferguson is one. _____

5 He plays at the back. _____

| thirsty | birth | stir | first | shirt |

6 Every footballer wears one. _____

7 When you need a drink. _____

8 To mix up. _____

9 The opposite of last. _____

10 To be born. _____

Answers

The alphabet.........................4–5
Practise your skills
All letters should be joined up in the correct order.

Big Match 1
1 d **2** i **3** n **4** q **5** w **6** e **7** j **8** n
9 s **10** w

Word-building 6–7
Practise your skills
A **1** bag **2** fan **3** wet **4** sit **5** cup **6** net
B **1** cup **2** wet **3** bag **4** fan **5** net **6** sit

Big Match 2
1 cap **2** leg **3** win **4** hit **5** lob
6 nod **7** box **8** sub **9** mud **10** hat

Word endings 8–9
Practise your skills
A **1** ball **2** wall **3** fall **4** off
   5 miss **6** toss
B **1** make a wall **2** take a fall **3** kick a ball
   4 toss a coin **5** miss a penalty **6** send off

Big Match 3
1 ball – call **2** fill – will **3** sell – yell
4 doll – loll **5** bull – pull **6** huff – puff
7 sniff – cliff **8** mess – less **9** hiss – kiss
10 boss – moss

Ch and sh words........................10–11
Practise your skills
1 chip chin chest catch pitch
2 shot ship shock rush wish

Big Match 4
1 chest **2** bench **3** child **4** chat **5** match
6 rush **7** shop **8** shin **9** cash **10** shut

Vowels and consonants............12–13
Practise your skills
1 Fred **2** kick **3** clap
4 hug **5** spot **6** sing

Big Match 5
1 Wes Brown **2** Nicky Butt
3 David Beckham **4** Andy Cole
5 Ryan Giggs **6** Roy Keane
7 Gary Neville **8** Paul Scholes
9 Dwight Yorke **10** Luke Chadwick

Double vowels ee and oo.........14–15
Practise your skills
Order of answers may differ.
1 see **2** food **3** week **4** deep
5 cool **6** feel **7** soon **8** roof

Big Match 6
1 three **2** moon **3** keep **4** mood **5** root
6 green **7** broom **8** sweet
9 cheek **10** proof

Magic e 16–17
Practise your skills
1 cape, tape, scrape **2** wine, shine, spine
3 robe, hope, note **4** use, tube, cute

Big Match 7
1 game – same **2** line – fine
3 stroke – joke **4** tube – cube
5 take – make **6** side – wide
7 time – crime **8** dive – five
9 bone – stone **10** fluke – duke

Answers

Words within words 18–19

Practise your skills

These are the most likely answers; other words may be possible.

1 Neville – ill, evil
2 Beckham – beck, ham, am
3 Irwin – win, in
4 Scholes – hole
5 Barthez – art, the
6 Fortune – for, or, fort, tune
7 Silvestre – vest
8 Chadwick – had, wick

Big Match 8

1 fish **2** cat **3** cow **4** hare **5** ant
6 owl **7** ape **8** fly **9** bat **10** lion

Common letter patterns – ea and oa 20–21

Practise your skills

```
              ¹g
 ²b o a s ³t   o
  e      e ⁴c o a t
  a   ⁵c o a c h   l
  t      m   e
            a
       ⁶s e a t
```

Big Match 9

1 goal **2** heat **3** coast **4** leap
5 speak **6** cloak **7** groan **8** steam
9 deal **10** soap

Compound words 22–23

Practise your skills

1 photograph **2** goalkeeper **3** turnstile
4 groundsman **5** bathtub **6** floodlights

Big Match 10

1 farmyard **2** runway **3** championship
4 airport **5** carpet **6** afternoon
7 overhead **8** butterfly **9** underground
10 motorway

Sound alike 24–25

Practise your skills

1 under over player swerve perfect
2 shirt dirty bird first girl

Big Match 11

1 goalkeeper **2** striker **3** referee
4 manager **5** defender **6** shirt
7 thirsty **8** stir **9** first **10** birth

Collect the set

Collect all 6 books and be an English and Maths champion.

Manchester United English

Louis Fidge

Manchester United Maths

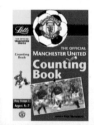  

Paul Broadbent

For all the latest news, views and information on

MANCHESTER UNITED®

visit the official Manchester United website:

WWW.MANUTD.COM

Manchester United Plc, Sir Matt Busby Way, Old Trafford, Manchester M16 0RA

Letts Educational, The Chiswick Centre, 414 Chiswick High Road, London W4 5TF
Tel: 020 8996 3333 Fax: 020 8742 8390 E-mail: mail@lettsed.co.uk
Website: www.letts-education.com

Published 2001
Text © Letts Educational Ltd. Published under license from Manchester United Football Club, Video Collection International Limited and Carlton Books Limited. All Trade Marks related to Manchester United Football Club are used with the permission of Manchester United Football Club, Video Collection International Limited and Carlton Books Limited.
Author: Louis Fidge
Editorial and Design: Moondisks Ltd, Cambridge
Illustrations: Joel Morris
Our thanks to Mark Wylie (MUFC museum curator) and John Peters (MUFC official photographer) for supplying material and their cooperation in the production of these books.

British Library Cataloguing in Publication Data
A CIP record for this book is available from the British Library.

ISBN 1-85805-982-8

Printed in Italy.

Letts Educational Limited is a member of Granada Learning Limited, part of the Granada Media Group.